Budgeting

Workbook

second edition

Aubrey Penning

osborne
BOOKS

Published by Osborne Books Limited
Unit 1B Everoak Estate
Bromyard Road
Worcester WR2 5HP
Tel 01905 748071
Email books@osbornebooks.co.uk
Website www.osbornebooks.co.uk

Design by Laura Ingham
Cover and page design image © Istockphoto.com/Petrovich9

Printed and bound by CPI Group (UK) Ltd, Croydon, CR0 4YY

British Library Cataloguing in Publication Data
A catalogue record for this book is available from the British Library

ISBN 978 1905777 839

Contents

Chapter activities

Chapter activities – answers

Practice assessments

Practice assessments – answers

Acknowledgements

The authors wish to thank the following for their help with the production of the book: Maz Loton, Jon Moore and Cathy Turner. Thanks are also due to Lynn Watkins for her technical editing and to Laura Ingham for her designs for this new series.

The publisher is indebted to the Association of Accounting Technicians for its kind permission to reproduce sample practice assessment material.

Author

Aubrey Penning has many years experience of teaching accountancy on a variety of courses in Worcester and Gwent. He is a Certified Accountant, and before his move into full-time teaching he worked for the health service, a housing association and a chemical supplier. Until recently he was the AAT course coordinator at Worcester College of Technology, specialising in the areas of management accounting and taxation.

Introduction

what this book covers

This book has been written specifically to cover the Learning Area 'Budgeting' which covers two QCF Units in the AAT Level 4 Diploma in Accounting:

- Principles of budgeting
- Drafting budgets

what this book contains

This book is set out in two sections:

- **Chapter activities** which provide extra practice material in addition to the activities included in the Osborne Books Tutorial text. Answers to the Chapter activities are set out in this book.
- **Practice Assessments** are included to prepare the student for the Computer Based Assessments. They are based directly on the structure, style and content of the sample assessment material provided by the AAT at www.aat.org.uk. Suggested answers to the Practice Assessments are set out in this book.

online support from Osborne Books

This book is supported by practice material available at www.osbornebooks.co.uk

This material is available to tutors – and to students at their discretion – in two forms:

- A **Tutor Zone** which is available to tutors who have adopted the Osborne Books texts. This area of the website provides extra assessment practice material (plus answers) in addition to the activities included in this Workbook text.
- **Online learning** – online practice questions designed to familiarise students with the style of the AAT Computer Based Assessments.

  Scan the code on the right using your Smartphone to gain access to the online practice questions.

further information

If you want to know more about our products, please visit www.osbornebooks.co.uk, email books@osbornebooks.co.uk or telephone Osborne Books Customer Services on 01905 748071.

Chapter activities

1 Chapter activities
The budgeting environment

1.1 Match the data in the first column with the appropriate source selected from the second column.

Data
Social trends in UK
Views of prospective customers
Current material costs
Competitors' performance

Source
Production Schedule
Office for National Statistics
Market Research
SWOT analysis
HMRC website
Financial press
Suppliers' quotations

1.2 Select an appropriate accounting system to deal with each of the following situations:

(a)	Manufacturing production process with high overheads and set-up costs	
(b)	Labour intensive manufacturing industry	
(c)	Budgeting for a manufacturing organisation where future output level is very uncertain	
(d)	Machine intensive production process with known output levels and long production runs	

Options:

1   Absorption costing using labour hours to absorb overheads

2   Marginal costing

3   Activity based costing

4   Absorption costing using machine hours to absorb overheads

1.3   Calculate the appropriate budgeted overhead recovery rate for the following production department. The department's annual budget for indirect costs is:

	£
Indirect labour	38,500
Supervisor wages	19,500
Depreciation of equipment	4,000
Machine maintenance	6,780
Canteen subsidy	11,220
Total	**80,000**

Notes: The budget production of 3,000 units will require 8,000 machine hours and 40,000 direct labour hours.

Complete the following:

Overhead recovery should be based on **Labour hours / Machine hours**

The recovery rate will be ⬚ per ⬚

1.4   Calculate the appropriate budgeted overhead recovery rate for the following production department. The department's annual budget for indirect costs is:

	£
Indirect labour	18,000
Supervisor wages	21,900
Depreciation of equipment	35,000
Machine maintenance	23,500
Canteen subsidy	3,600
Total	**102,000**

Notes: The budget production of 5,000 units will require 12,750 machine hours and 1,020 direct labour hours.

Complete the following:

Overhead recovery should be based on **Labour hours / Machine hours**

The recovery rate will be ⬚ per ⬚

1.5 A company wishes to estimate how its overheads behave when production volumes change.

(a) Complete the following table, and by using the high-low method calculate the expected variable costs (per unit) and fixed costs (per month).

	Cost per month £	Output per month (units)
Data provided	70,000	10,000
Data provided	90,000	14,000
Difference		
Variable cost per unit		
Fixed cost per month		

(b) Using the information calculated in part (a), complete the following table to show the breakdown of estimated costs at a monthly production level of 13,500 units.

	£
Variable costs	
Fixed costs	
Total costs	

2 Chapter activities
Forecasting techniques

2.1 This year's sales are £1,500,000. Analysis of recent years shows:

■ a growth trend of 3% per annum

■ seasonal variations from the trend of

quarter 1	-£50,000
quarter 2	+£10,000
quarter 3	+£75,000
quarter 4	-£35,000

Forecast the sales for each quarter of next year, using the following table.

	£
Quarter 1	
Quarter 2	
Quarter 3	
Quarter 4	
Total Sales	

2.2 Next year's sales were originally forecast at £5,414,850, assuming a 5% selling price increase from this year. The increase has now been agreed at 3% instead. Assuming the sales volume does not alter from the original forecast, calculate the revised sales forecast.

		✓
(a)	£5,306,553	
(b)	£5,311,710	
(c)	£5,577,296	
(d)	£5,253,405	

2.3   Electricity costs for the last year were £240,000, based on a price of 10p per kWh used. The forecast for next year shows a reduction in consumption of 5% due to energy saving measures, but a price increase of 8%. Using the following table, calculate the electricity budget for next year. Do not round any figures.

Current year's usage (kWh)	
Next year's usage (kWh)	
Current year's price per kWh (£)	
Next year's price per kWh (£)	
Budget for electricity next year (£)	

2.4   The budget for the cost of gas for next year was originally set at £121,000. This assumed a 10% increase in costs from last year, and assumed that consumption would not change.

It is now believed that the unit cost will increase by 7% from last year, but that consumption will increase by 4%.

Complete the following:

The cost of gas last year was   £ [ ]

Allowing for both a change in consumption and a price increase, the budget for next year should be

£ [ ]

2.5   The trend in the number of units sold per quarter was 7,400 in the last quarter of the current year. The trend increases by 50 units per quarter.

The seasonal variations are a percentage of the trend for the quarter, and have been established as

quarter 1   -10%

quarter 2   -15%

quarter 3   +35%

quarter 4   -10%

The selling price for each unit will be £22 in the next year. Complete the following table to establish the data for the sales budget for next year. Calculate the unit forecast to the nearest whole unit.

	Trend (units)	Forecast (units)	Forecast sales £
Quarter 1			
Quarter 2			
Quarter 3			
Quarter 4			
Totals			

3

Chapter activities
Preparing budgets – the main principles

3.1 Complete the following table by using ticks to show into which budget each item of cost would occur.

✓

	Cost of Production	Maintenance	Capital Expenditure	Marketing	Finance
Direct labour wages	✓				
Interest charges					✓
New computer system			✓		
Entertaining customers				✓	
Hire of machinery testing equipment		✓			
Raw materials usage	✓				

3.2 Complete the following table to show the forecast inventories and production units for a particular product.

Closing inventory should be 40% of the following week's forecast sales

Number of Units	Week 1	Week 2	Week 3	Week 4	Week 5
Opening inventory	4,000	5000	4400	4200	4800
Production ③	11,000 ~~13,500~~	11900	10800	11,100	11200
Sub total ②	15,000	16900	15 200	15300	16,000
Forecast sales	10,000	12,500	11,000	10,500	12,000
Closing inventory ①	12,500×40% = 5000	11,000×40% = 4,400	4200	4800	10000×40% = 4000

Forecast sales in week 6 are 10,000 units.

3.3 The following production budget for a month has been prepared.

Production Budget	Units
Opening inventory of finished goods	5,000
Production	40,000
Sub total	45,000
Sales	38,000
Closing inventory of finished goods	7,000

(a) Complete the following working schedule for raw materials. Each unit produced requires 0.75 kg of material. Closing inventory is valued at budgeted purchase price.

Raw Materials	kg	£
Opening inventory of raw materials	3,500	7,000
Purchases of raw materials =£2	32,000	64,000
Sub total	35,500	71,000
Used in production 40000 × 0.75kg	30,000	60,000
Closing inventory of raw materials	∴ 5,500	£2 11,000

(handwritten right margin:)
kg   £
3,500   7000
26,500 × 2   ~~73,000~~ 53,000
40,000   60,000

(b) Complete the following working schedule for direct labour. Each unit takes 6 minutes to make. There are 22 direct labour employees, each working 160 basic hours in the month. Additional hours are paid at an overtime rate of time and a half. The overtime premium is included in the direct labour cost.   40,000 units × 6 ÷ 60 = 4000hrs production

(handwritten left margin:) 22 × 160 =

Direct Labour	Hours	Cost £
Basic time at £10 per hour 22 × 160	3520	35200
Overtime ∴	480 ×15	7200
Total	4000	42400

(c) Complete the following working schedule for overheads. Variable overheads are recovered based on total labour hours worked.

Overheads	Hours	Cost £
Variable overheads at £2.00 per hour	4000	8000
Fixed overheads		12,000
Total overheads		20,000

continued

(d) Complete the following operating budget, using information from the earlier tasks. Closing inventory of finished goods is to be valued at budgeted production cost per unit.

Operating Budget	Units	£ per unit	£
Sales	38,000	4.50	171,000
Cost of Goods Sold:			
Opening inventory of finished goods			15,300
Cost of production:		£	
Raw Materials		60,000	
Direct Labour		42,400	
Production Overheads		20,000	
Total cost of production			122,400
Closing inventory of finished goods 122,400 ÷ 40000 × ~~5500~~ 7000			21420
Cost of goods sold			116 280
Gross profit			54720
Non-production overheads		£	
Administration		15,000	
Marketing		12,500	
Total non-production overheads			27500
Net profit			27220

3.4 The following budget data has been prepared.

Budget Data	June £	July £	August £	Sept £
Credit Sales	8,900	8,300	8,800	9,500
Purchases	4,200	5,100	4,800	4,900
Wages	2,300	2,350	2,300	2,400
Expenses	1,050	1,080	1,070	1,090
Capital expenditure	2,000		4,500	

Timings:

60% of credit sales are received in the month after sale, the remainder 1 month later

Purchases are paid in the month after purchase

Wages are paid in the month incurred

Expenses are paid in the month after they are incurred. Expenses include £200 per month depreciation.

Capital expenditure is paid immediately it is incurred

Complete a cash forecast for August, using the following table.

Cash Forecast - August	£
Opening cash balance	16,400
Receipts from sales June 40% x 8900 = July 60% x 8300=	3560 ~~3340~~ ~~8650~~ ~~3320~~ } ~~8650~~ £ 8540
Payments for:	4980
Purchases July	5100
Wages Aug	2300
Expenses July 1080 – 200 depn	880
Capital expenditure Aug	4500
Total payments	12,780
Closing cash balance	12,160

4 Chapter activities
Preparing budgets – dealing with resources

4.1 The number of units of a product that are required are shown below. 5% of the units produced fail a quality control test and are scrapped. Complete the table to show the number of units that must be manufactured to allow for this rejection rate.

	Month 1	Month 2	Month 3
Required units	76,000	77,900	81,700
Manufactured units	$76,000 \times \frac{100}{95}$ $= 80,000$	$77,900 \times \frac{100}{95}$ $= 82,000$	$81,700 \times \frac{100}{95}$ $= 86,000$

4.2 19,000 units of finished product are to be manufactured in September. Each finished unit contains 3 kg of raw material. 5% of the raw material input is wasted during production. Inventories of raw material are to be:

■ opening inventory 30,000 kg

■ closing inventory 25,000 kg

Select the quantity of raw material to be purchased from the following:

		✓
(a)	55,000 kg	✓
(b)	57,000 kg	
(c)	54,850 kg	
(d)	49,150 kg	

Amount required:

19,000 × 3 = 57,000 kg

+ lost wastages

$57,000 \times \frac{100}{95} = 60,000$

Required 60,000
Less OI (30,000)
Plus CI 25,000 = 55,000 kg

4.3 24,000 units of finished product are to be manufactured during October. Each unit takes 4 minutes to produce. 9 staff each work 160 basic hours in October.

The number of overtime hours required to be worked in October is **160 hrs**

$24,000 \times \frac{4}{60} = 1,600$ hrs production needed

9 × 160 = 1440 hrs basic time available

∴ 1600 − 1440 = 160 hrs o/t needed

4.4 Department K manufactures three products, Alpha, Beta and Gamma.

Calculate the machine hours required to manufacture these in November, using the following table.

Product	Units	Hours per unit	Hours required
Alpha	190	✗ 1.0	190
Beta	200	✗ 2.5	500
Gamma	270	✗ 3.2	864
Total machine hours for department K			1554

There are three machines in the department.

Each machine can be used for 350 hours in November. Additional machines can be hired if required.

How many additional machines should be hired? $\boxed{\text{2}}$

1554/350 = 4.44
=
5 mach
total
neoded

4.5 The following information is available about a company that makes a single product.

- Each unit is made from 1.5 kg of material costing £1.80 per kg.
- It takes 15 minutes to make each item.
- 800 hours of basic labour time is available in the month of April. Any extra hours must be worked in overtime.
- The basic labour rate is £12 per hour. Overtime is paid at time and a half (50% more than basic rate).
- Variable overhead relates to labour hours worked, including overtime.
- Fixed overhead costs are incurred evenly through the year.

Complete the following table with the April budget figures.

	Budget for the year	Budget for April
Units sold	36,000	3,000
Units produced	40,000	3,500
	£	£
Sales	540,000	45,000
Cost of production:		
Materials used	108,000	9450
Labour	122,400	10950
Variable production overhead	20,000	1750
Fixed production overhead	18,000	1500

Handwritten annotations:
- Units sold: *540/36 £15 per unit*
- Sales (April): *£15 × 3000 = 45,000*
- Year Variable production overhead: *40,000÷2 = 20,000*
- Materials used (April): *3500 × 1.5 × 1.8 = 9450*
- Labour (year): *800 × 4 = 3200 = units basic ∴ 300 o/t = 75 hrs*
- Labour (April): *800 × 12 = 9600, 75 × 18 = 1350, = 10950*
- Variable production overhead (April): *3500 ÷ 2 = 1750*
- Fixed production overhead (April): *18,000 ÷ 12 = 1500*

5

Chapter activities

Monitoring performance with budgets

5.1   You have prepared a draft budget for direct material costs.

- It is based on the current usage of material per unit produced, together with the current cost per kilo plus an expected cost increase.

- The purchasing manager has forecast the cost increase.

- You have calculated the total required material usage from the agreed production budget.

- You understand that there are no planned changes to raw material inventory levels.

- You have been asked to suggest appropriate performance measures that would assist managers to monitor direct material costs against budget.

Direct material budget

	This year	Next year budget
Production units	430,000	500,000
Raw materials per unit (kg)	0.35	0.35
Total raw material usage (kg)	150,500	175,000
Cost of raw materials used (£)	£1,053,500	£1,261,750

Write an email to the Production Director:

(a)   Explaining the calculations and assumptions and requesting his approval.

(b)   Suggesting appropriate direct material performance indicators for this department.

email
to:
from:
date:
subject

5.2 The operating statement that forms part of the following table has been produced, using the original fixed budget (based on production and sales of 50,000 units) and the actual costs which occurred when 60,000 units were produced and sold.

Using the data in the operating statement, together with the notes shown below, complete the flexed budget and variances in the appropriate columns in the table.

	Original Budget	Actual	Flexed Budget	Variances Fav / (Adv)
Volume (units)	50,000	60,000	60,000	
	£	£	£	£
Turnover	2,250,000	2,640,000		
Costs:				
Materials	600,000	780,000		
Labour	750,000	895,000		
Distribution	200,000	255,000		
Energy	79,000	85,000		
Equipment hire	15,000	22,000		
Depreciation	24,000	24,000		
Marketing	28,000	30,000		
Administration	45,000	44,500		
Total Costs	1,741,000	2,135,500		
Operating Profit	509,000	504,500		

Notes on budget

- Material, labour and distribution costs are variable
- The budget for energy is semi-variable. The fixed element is £4,000
- Equipment hire budget is based on a cost of £3,000 for each 11,000 units or fewer
- Depreciation, marketing and administration costs are fixed

5.3   The following operating statement has been prepared using marginal costing and a flexed budget.

Operating Statement for November	Budget £	Actual £	Variance £ Fav / (Adv)
Turnover	96,000	88,000	(8,000)
Variable costs:			
Materials	32,000	30,000	2,000
Labour	16,000	19,000	(3,000)
Distribution	8,000	8,200	(200)
Power	6,000	5,900	100
Contribution	**34,000**	**24,900**	**(9,100)**
Fixed costs:			
Power	2,500	3,000	(500)
Depreciation	3,500	3,300	200
Marketing	5,000	4,500	500
Administration	6,500	6,500	0
Operating Profit	**16,500**	**7,600**	**(8,900)**

The original budget was based on producing and selling 1,500 units. The company actually produced and sold 1,600 units, and the budget was flexed to this volume.

You have also established the following information about the operations:

■   the quantity of material used was in line with the output produced

■   employees worked overtime to cope with the additional output

■   there was a change in both fixed and variable power costs imposed by the power supply company

■   some non-current assets were sold for their book value; this was not originally planned

continued

Select from the following statements, those that are consistent with the operating statement and information shown above and could form part of a report.

✓

(a) The turnover variance was caused by the difference between the original budgeted output and the actual output.	
(b) The turnover variance was caused by selling at a lower average price than budgeted (£55 instead of £60). This may have helped increase the sales from the original budget.	
(c) The favourable material variance could have been caused by either using fewer materials than planned or by obtaining the materials at a cheaper price, or a combination of these factors.	
(d) Since the quantity of materials used was in line with the output, the material cost variance must have been caused by paying a higher price than budgeted for the materials.	
(e) Since the quantity of materials used was in line with the output, the material cost variance must have been caused by paying a lower price than budgeted for the materials.	
(f) A possible cause of the adverse labour cost variance is the need to use overtime hours, which are probably paid at a higher rate than basic hours.	
(g) The labour cost variance may be entirely caused by the difference between the original budgeted output and the actual (higher) output.	
(h) The changes in the power tariff have resulted in less cost overall for power than was budgeted.	
(i) The changes in the power tariff mean that a greater element of the cost is fixed than budgeted, although the variable element seems to have decreased. Overall the total power cost has increased.	
(j) The depreciation charge is decreased due to the profit on sale of the non-current assets.	
(k) The actual depreciation charge is lower than that budgeted since some non-current assets were sold, and are therefore no longer depreciated.	
(l) The overall operating profit adverse variance is mainly accounted for by the reduction in average selling price compared to budget.	

5.4   Unsure Limited originally produced two budgets, one based on an output of 10,000 units, and one based on an output of 15,000 units. The actual output (production and sales) was 11,500 units.

Complete the following table with a flexed budget and variances based on the flexed budget.

	Budget 1	Budget 2	Actual	Flexed Budget	Variances Fav / (Adv)
Units	10,000	15,000	11,500	11,500	
	£	£	£	£	£
Sales	900,000	1,350,000	1,058,000		
Materials	250,000	375,000	299,000		
Labour	350,000	500,000	380,000		
Production Overheads	170,000	195,000	190,000		
Administration Overheads	60,000	60,000	62,000		
Operating Profit	70,000	220,000	127,000		

Answers to chapter activities

1 Chapter activities – answers
The budgeting environment

1.1

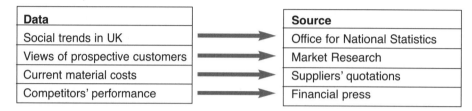

Data		Source
Social trends in UK	→	Office for National Statistics
Views of prospective customers	→	Market Research
Current material costs	→	Suppliers' quotations
Competitors' performance	→	Financial press

1.2　(a)　**3**

　　　(b)　**1**

　　　(c)　**2**

　　　(d)　**4**

1.3　Overhead recovery should be based on **Labour hours**

　　　The recovery rate will be £2.00 per direct labour hour.

1.4　Overhead recovery should be based on **Machine hours**

　　　The recovery rate will be £8.00 per machine hour.

1.5　**(a)**

	Cost per Month £	Output per month (units)
Data provided	70,000	10,000
Data provided	90,000	14,000
Difference	20,000	4,000
Variable cost per unit	£5.00	
Fixed cost per month	£20,000	

(b)

	£
Variable costs	67,500
Fixed costs	20,000
Total costs	87,500

2 Chapter activities – answers
Forecasting techniques

2.1

	£
Quarter 1	336,250
Quarter 2	396,250
Quarter 3	461,250
Quarter 4	351,250
Total Sales	1,545,000

2.2   (b)   £5,311,710

2.3

Current year's usage (kWh)	2,400,000
Next year's usage (kWh)	2,280,000
Current year's price per kWh (£)	0.10
Next year's price per kWh (£)	0.108
Budget for electricity next year (£)	246,240

2.4   The cost of gas last year was £110,000

Allowing for both a change in consumption and a price increase, the budget for next year should be £122,408

2.5

	Trend (units)	Forecast (units)	Forecast sales £
Quarter 1	7,450	6,705	147,510
Quarter 2	7,500	6,375	140,250
Quarter 3	7,550	10,193	224,246
Quarter 4	7,600	6,840	150,480
Total		30,113	662,486

3

Chapter activities – answers
Preparing budgets – the main principles

3.1

	Cost of Production	Maintenance	Capital Expenditure	Marketing	Finance
Direct labour wages	✓				
Interest charges					✓
New computer system			✓		
Entertaining customers				✓	
Hire of machinery testing equipment		✓			
Raw materials usage	✓				

3.2

Number of Units	Week 1	Week 2	Week 3	Week 4	Week 5
Opening inventory	4,000	5,000	4,400	4,200	4,800
Production	11,000	11,900	10,800	11,100	11,200
Sub total	15,000	16,900	15,200	15,300	16,000
Forecast sales	10,000	12,500	11,000	10,500	12,000
Closing inventory	5,000	4,400	4,200	4,800	4,000

3.3 **(a)**

Raw Materials	kg	£
Opening inventory of raw materials	3,500	7,000
Purchases of raw materials	32,000	64,000
Sub total	35,500	71,000
Used in production	30,000	60,000
Closing inventory of raw materials	5,500	11,000

(b)

Direct Labour	Hours	Cost £
Basic time at £10 per hour	3,520	35,200
Overtime	480	7,200
Total	4,000	42,400

(c)

Overheads	Hours	Cost £
Variable overheads at £2.00 per hour	4,000	8,000
Fixed overheads		12,000
Total overheads		20,000

(d)

Operating Budget	Units	£ per unit	£
Sales	38,000	4.50	171,000
Cost of Goods Sold:			
Opening inventory of finished goods			15,300
Cost of production:		£	
Raw Materials		60,000	
Direct Labour		42,400	
Production Overheads		20,000	
Total cost of production			122,400
Closing inventory of finished goods			21,420
Cost of goods sold			116,280
Gross profit			54,720
Non-production overheads		£	
Administration		15,000	
Marketing		12,500	
Total non-production overheads			27,500
Net profit			27,220

3.4

Cash Forecast – August	£
Opening cash balance	16,400
Receipts from sales	8,540
Payments for:	
Purchases	5,100
Wages	2,300
Expenses	880
Capital expenditure	4,500
Total payments	12,780
Closing cash balance	12,160

Chapter activities – answers
Preparing budgets – dealing with resources

4.1

	Month 1	Month 2	Month 3
Required units	76,000	77,900	81,700
Manufactured units	80,000	82,000	86,000

4.2 (a) 55,000 kg

4.3 The number of overtime hours required to be worked in October is 160 hours

4.4

Product	Units	Hours per unit	Hours required
Alpha	190	1.0	190
Beta	200	2.5	500
Gamma	270	3.2	864
Total machine hours for department K			1,554

2 additional machines should be hired.

4.5

	Budget for the year	Budget for April
Units sold	36,000	3,000
Units produced	40,000	3,500
	£	£
Sales	540,000	45,000
Cost of production:		
Materials used	108,000	9,450
Labour	122,400	10,950
Variable production overhead	20,000	1,750
Fixed production overhead	18,000	1,500

5

Chapter activities – answers
Monitoring performance with budgets

5.1 **(a)** and **(b)**

---

email

to: Production Director

from: Accounting Technician

date: xx

subject: Direct Material Budget

Budget Submission

I enclose the proposed direct material budget for your consideration and approval.

The production budget is based on an increase from the current output of 430,000 units to 500,000 units next year, and this assumption has been used for the direct material budget.

The budget assumes the current usage of raw material per unit produced (0.35kg per unit) will be maintained. It allows for a cost increase of raw materials of 3% from the current level of £7.00 per kg to £7.21 per kg. This cost increase has been provided by the purchasing manager.

Since there is no planned change in the raw material inventory levels, the quantity of material to be purchased will be the same as the budgeted usage.

Please let me know if you need any further information.

Performance Indicators

There are several possible measures to monitor usage and cost of raw materials. We should monitor on a weekly or monthly basis:

- raw material usage per unit produced

- raw material cost per unit produced

- number of faulty units produced due to raw material quality (if any)

If a standard costing system was to be introduced throughout the company, the direct material variances would also prove invaluable for monitoring performance.

5.2

	Original Budget	Actual	Flexe		
Volume (units)	50,000	60,000			
	£	£			
Turnover	2,250,000	2,640,000	2,700,000	(৬৬,৴৴৴)	
Costs:					
Materials	600,000	780,000	720,000	(60,000)	
Labour	750,000	895,000	900,000	5,000	
Distribution	200,000	255,000	240,000	(15,000)	
Energy	79,000	85,000	94,000	9,000	
Equipment hire	15,000	22,000	18,000	(4,000)	
Depreciation	24,000	24,000	24,000	0	
Marketing	28,000	30,000	28,000	(2,000)	
Administration	45,000	44,500	45,000	500	
Total Costs	1,741,000	2,135,500	2,069,000	(66,500)	
Operating Profit	509,000	504,500	631,000	(126,500)	

5.3 The following statements are consistent with the operating statement and information provided and could form part of a report.

(b), (e), (f), (i), (k) and (l)

	Budget 1	Budget 2	Actual	Flexed Budget	Variances Fav / (Adv)
Units	10,000	15,000	11,500	11,500	
	£	£	£	£	£
Sales	900,000	1,350,000	1,058,000	1,035,000	23,000
Materials	250,000	375,000	299,000	287,500	(11,500)
Labour	350,000	500,000	380,000	395,000	15,000
Production Overheads	170,000	195,000	190,000	177,500	(12,500)
Administration Overheads	60,000	60,000	62,000	60,000	(2,000)
Operating Profit	70,000	220,000	127,000	115,000	12,000

Flexed Budget Workings:

Sales   Selling price is £90 per unit x 11,500 units = £1,035,000

Materials   Variable cost of £25 per unit x 11,500 units = £287,500

Labour   Semi-variable cost: use high-low method

    Variable (£500,000 - £350,000) / (15,000 – 10,000 units)

    = £30 per unit

    Fixed = £350,000 – (£30 x 10,000) = £50,000

Production Overheads   Semi-variable cost: use high-low method

    Variable (£195,000 - £170,000) / (15,000 – 10,000 units)

    = £5 per unit

    Fixed = £170,000 – (£5 x 10,000) = £120,000

Budgeting

Practice assessment 1

Section 1

Task 1.1

(a)

Match the data in the first column with the appropriate source selected from the second column.

Data
Typical performance in the trade
National economic growth
Corporation tax rates

Source
SWOT Analysis
Supplier price lists
Trade association publications
Market research
HMRC publications
Office for National Statistics

(b)

Who would you contact in each of the following situations?

(a)	You want to know details of planned pay rises	
(b)	You want details of the sales forecast	
(c)	You want details of planned acquisitions of non-current assets	

Select from:

1   Capital expenditure budget working group

2   Production director

3   Purchasing manager

4   Sales director

5   Human resources manager

6   Marketing manager

(c)

Complete the following table by using ticks to show into which budget(s) each item of cost would occur. ✓

	Direct Cost of Production	Production Overheads	Capital Expenditure	Marketing	Cash
Extension to offices					
Depreciation of production equipment					
Indirect production labour					
Advertising campaign costs					
Hire of production equipment					
Printing customer perceptions questionnaire					

(d)

Select an appropriate accounting treatment for each of the following costs from the options available.

(a)	Employers' national insurance for administration staff	
(b)	Material usage for production	
(c)	Rent of photocopier	
(d)	Cost of the stores department	
(e)	Cost of idle time for production operatives	
(f)	Cost of productive time for production operatives	

Options available are:

1   Activity based charge to production cost centres

2   Allocate to administration overheads

3   Direct cost

4   Allocate to finance overheads

5   Allocate to selling and distribution overheads

6   Allocate to production overheads

(e)

Calculate the appropriate budgeted overhead recovery rate for the following production department. The department's annual budget for indirect costs is:

	£
Indirect labour	36,000
Supervisor wages	43,800
Depreciation of machinery	70,000
Machine maintenance	47,000
Canteen subsidy	13,200
Total	**210,000**

Notes: The budget production of 5,000 units will require 13,125 machine hours and 1,050 direct labour hours.

Complete the following:

Overhead recovery should be based on Labour hours / Machine hours

The recovery rate will be ☐ per ☐

Task 1.2

(a)

Complete the following table to show the forecast inventories and production units for a particular product.

Closing inventory should be 25% of the following week's forecast sales.

Number of Units	Week 1	Week 2	Week 3	Week 4	Week 5
Opening inventory	5,000				
Production					
Sub total					
Forecast sales	20,000	21,500	21,000	20,500	22,000
Closing inventory					

Forecast sales in week 6 are 25,000 units.

(b)

The number of units of a product that are required are shown below. 7% of the units produced fail a quality control test and are scrapped. Complete the table to show the number of units that must be manufactured to allow for this rejection rate.

	Month 1	Month 2	Month 3
Required units	75,330	79,980	77,190
Manufactured units			

(c)

The following information is available about the plans for June

■   23,750 units of finished product are to be manufactured

■   Each unit of finished product contains 4.0 kg of raw material

■   5% of raw material is wasted during manufacture

■   The opening inventory of raw material is 18,000 kg

■   The closing inventory of raw material is to be 20,000 kg

The purchases of raw material must be

	✓
(a) 100,000 kg	
(b) 95,000 kg	
(c) 8,250 kg	
(d) 98,000 kg	
(e) 102,000 kg	
(f) 101,750 kg	

(d)

50,000 units of finished product are to be manufactured during October. Each unit takes 3 minutes to produce. 12 staff each work 180 basic hours in October.

Complete the following sentences:

The number of units that can be made in basic time during October is

The number of overtime hours required to be worked in October is

(e)

Department G manufactures three products, Aye, Bee and Cee.

Calculate the machine hours required to manufacture these in November, using the following table.

Product	Units	Units per hour	Hours required
Aye	1,920	8	
Bee	1,200	2.5	
Cee	1,400	5	
Total machine hours for department G			

There are three machines in the department.

Each machine can be used for 300 hours in November. Additional machines can be hired if required.

How many additional machines should be hired?

Task 1.3

The following production budget for a month has been prepared.

Production Budget	Units
Opening inventory of finished goods	3,000
Production	28,000
Sub total	31,000
Sales	30,000
Closing inventory of finished goods	1,000

(a) Complete the following working schedule for raw materials. Each unit produced requires 1.25 kg of material. Closing inventory is valued at budgeted purchase price.

Raw Materials	kg	£
Opening inventory of raw materials	1,800	7,200
Purchases of raw materials	34,000	136,000
Sub total	35,800	143,200
Used in production		
Closing inventory of raw materials		

(b) Complete the following working schedule for direct labour. Each unit takes 7.5 minutes to make. There are 20 direct labour employees, each working 160 basic hours in the month. Additional hours are paid at an overtime rate of time and a half. The overtime premium is included in the direct labour cost.

Direct Labour	Hours	Cost £
Basic time at £14 per hour		
Overtime		
Total		

(c) Complete the following working schedule for overheads. Variable overheads are recovered based on total labour hours worked.

Overheads	Hours	Cost £
Variable overheads at £9.00 per hour		
Fixed overheads		24,500
Total overheads		

(d) Complete the following operating budget, using information from the earlier tasks. Closing inventory of finished goods is to be valued at budgeted production cost per unit.

Operating Budget	Units	£ per unit	£
Sales		10.50	
Cost of Goods Sold:			
Opening inventory of finished goods			26,475
Cost of production:		£	
Raw Materials			
Direct Labour			
Production Overheads			
Total cost of production			
Closing inventory of finished goods			
Cost of goods sold			
Gross profit			
Non-production overheads		£	
Administration		18,000	
Marketing		13,500	
Total non-production overheads			
Net profit			

Task 1.4

(a)

This year's sales are £2,500,000. Analysis of recent years shows:

- a growth trend of 2.5% per annum
- seasonal variations from the trend of

    quarter 1   -£40,000

    quarter 2   +£20,000

    quarter 3   +£55,000

    quarter 4   -£35,000

Forecast the sales for each quarter of next year, using the following table.

	£
Quarter 1	
Quarter 2	
Quarter 3	
Quarter 4	
Total Sales	

(b)

The following information is available about a company that makes a single product.

- Each unit is made from 2.5 kg of material costing £2.80 per kg.
- It takes 10 minutes to make each item.
- 1,200 hours of basic labour time is available in the month of May. Any extra hours must be worked in overtime.
- The basic labour rate is £10 per hour. Overtime is paid at time and a half (50% more than basic rate).
- Variable overhead relates to labour hours worked, including overtime.
- Fixed overhead costs are incurred evenly through the year.

Complete the following table with the May budget figures.

	Budget for the year	Budget for May
Units sold	105,000	9,000
Units produced	100,000	8,100
	£	£
Sales	1,260,000	108,000
Cost of production:		
Materials used	700,000	56,700
Labour	175,000	14,250
Variable production overhead	20,000	1,620
Fixed production overhead	48,000	4,000

(c)

The following budget data has been prepared.

Budget Data	June £	July £	August £	Sept £
Credit Sales	5,900	6,300	5,800	7,500
Purchases	3,200	2,100	2,800	2,900
Wages	1,500	2,000	1,630	1,900
Expenses	1,090	1,070	1,080	1,100
Capital expenditure		1,500	2,500	

Timings:

75% of credit sales are received in the month after sale, the remainder 1 month later

Purchases are paid in the month after purchase

Wages are paid in the month incurred

Expenses are paid in the month after they are incurred. Expenses include £350 per month depreciation.

Capital expenditure is paid immediately it is incurred

Complete a cash forecast for August, using the following table.

Cash Forecast - August	£
Opening cash balance	8,650
Receipts from sales	
Payments for:	
Purchases	
Wages	
Expenses	
Capital expenditure	
Total payments	
Closing cash balance	

Task 1.5

You have prepared a draft budget for direct material costs.

■   The company uses standard costing, and updates the standards annually.

■   The budget is based on the current standard cost of material, but the usage of material is based on a reduction in wastage due to new machinery.

■   The chief buyer has confirmed that prices are expected to remain stable.

■   The production manager has confirmed the percentage saving in usage that will be incorporated into the standard for next year.

■   You have calculated the total required material usage from the agreed production budget.

■   You understand that there are no planned changes to raw material inventory levels.

■   You have been asked to suggest appropriate performance measures that would assist managers to monitor direct material costs against budget.

Direct material budget

	This year	Next year budget
Production units	250,000	240,000
Standard quantity of materials per unit (kg)	0.75	0.735
Total material usage (kg)	187,500	176,400
Cost of raw materials used (£)	£1,368,750	£1,287,720

Write an email to the Production Director:

(a)   Explaining the calculations and assumptions and requesting his approval.

(b)   Suggesting appropriate direct material performance indicators for this department.

email

to:

from:

date:

subject:

Section 2

Task 2.1

(a)

A company has budgeted to make and sell 60,000 units in the coming year.

Each unit takes 20 minutes to make and requires 2.5kg of raw material. The quality control department can test 4,200 units each month. A contract has been placed to purchase 100,000kg of raw material at an agreed price. Further supplies can be obtained on the open market but the price is likely to be much higher. The company employs 10 production workers. Each worker works 1,750 hours a year in normal time.

Complete the following analysis.

There is labour available to make _____ units in normal time. Therefore, _____ hours of overtime will be needed.

The raw material contract will provide enough material to make _____ units.

Therefore, _____kg will have to be purchased on the open market.

Quality control can test _____ units in the year. It will be necessary to make alternative arrangements for _____ units.

(b)

Next year's sales were originally forecast at £5,414,850, assuming a 5% selling price increase from this year. It has now been agreed that there will be no price increase. Assuming the sales volume does not alter from the original forecast, calculate the revised sales forecast.

		✓
(a)	£5,144,108	
(b)	£5,685,593	
(c)	£5,157,000	
(d)	£5,699,842	

(c)

Electricity costs for the last year were £308,000, based on a price of 11p per kWh used. The forecast for next year shows a reduction in consumption of 4% due to energy saving measures, but a price increase of 10%. Using the following table, calculate the electricity budget for next year. Do not round any figures.

Current year's usage (kWh)	
Next year's usage (kWh)	
Current year's price per kWh (£)	
Next year's price per kWh (£)	
Budget for electricity next year (£)	

Task 2.2

The operating statement that forms part of the following table has been produced using the original fixed budget (based on production and sales of 90,000 units) and the actual costs which occurred when 80,000 units were produced and sold.

Using the data in the operating statement, together with the notes shown below, complete the flexed budget and variances in the appropriate columns in the table.

	Original Budget	Actual	Flexed Budget	Variances Fav / (Adv)
Volume (units)	90,000	80,000	80,000	
	£	£	£	£
Turnover	1,170,000	1,056,000	1,040,000	16,000
Costs:				
Materials	450,000	410,000	400,000	(10,000)
Labour	360,000	340,000	320,000	(20,000)
Distribution	180,000	155,000	160,000	5,000
Energy	55,000	55,000	50,000	(5,000)
Equipment hire	16,000	15,000	14,000	(1,000)
Depreciation	23,000	24,000	23,000	(1,000)
Marketing	21,000	20,000	21,000	1,000
Administration	25,000	24,000	25,000	1,000
Total Costs	1,130,000	1,043,000	1,013,000	(30,000)
Operating Profit	40,000	13,000	27,000	(14,000)

Notes on budget

■　Material, labour and distribution costs are variable

■　The budget for energy is semi-variable. The fixed element is £10,000

■　Equipment hire budget is based on a cost of £2,000 for each 12,000 units or fewer

■　Depreciation, marketing and administration costs are fixed

Task 2.3

The following operating statement has been prepared using marginal costing and a flexed budget.

Operating Statement for November	Budget £	Actual £	Variance £ Fav / (Adv)
Turnover	144,000	132,000	(12,000)
Variable costs:			
Materials	48,000	45,000	3,000
Labour	24,000	28,500	(4,500)
Distribution	12,000	12,000	0
Power	9,000	8,850	150
Contribution	**51,000**	**37,650**	**(13,350)**
Fixed costs:			
Power	3,750	4,500	(750)
Depreciation	5,250	4,950	300
Marketing	7,500	7,500	0
Administration	9,750	9,750	0
Operating Profit	**24,750**	**10,950**	**(13,800)**

The original budget was based on producing and selling 1,500 units. The company actually produced and sold 1,600 units, and the budget was flexed to this volume.

You have also established the following information about the operations:

■ the price of material was in line with the budgeted price

■ employees worked overtime to cope with the additional output

■ there was a change in both fixed and variable power costs imposed by the power supply company

■ the estimated remaining lives of some non-current assets were reassessed and extended

■ depreciation is calculated on a straight line basis

Write an email to the Managing Director that suggests possible reasons for each of the variances.

email

to:

from:

date:

subject:

Budgeting

Practice assessment 2

This Assessment is based on a sample assessment provided by the AAT and is reproduced here with their kind permission.

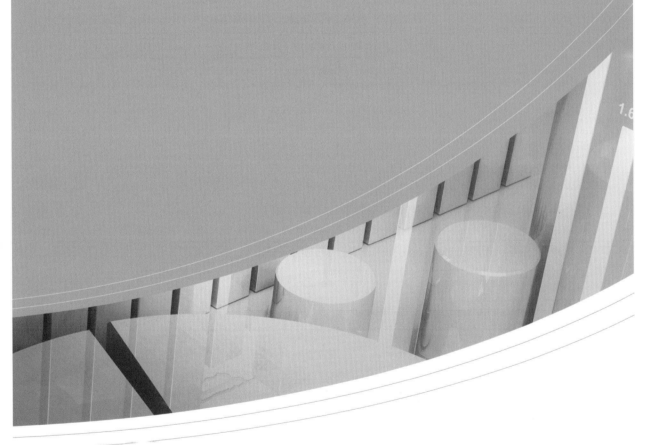

Section 1

Task 1.1

(a)

Match the data in the first column with the appropriate source selected from the second column.

Data
Inflation trends in UK
Value Added Tax (VAT) rates
Demand for our products

Source
Market Research
Office for National Statistics
SWOT analysis
HMRC publications (Her Majesty's Revenue & Customs)
Gross National Product
New York Times

(b)

Who would you contact in each of the following situations?

(a) You want to identify the production capacity of the firm.	
(b) You want to forecast the price of raw materials.	
(c) The draft budget is ready for review.	

Select from:

1 Trade union representative

2 Managing director

3 Buyer

4 Budget committee

5 Production planning manager

(c)

Complete the following table by using ticks to show into which budget(s) each item of cost would occur. ✓

	Personnel	Cost of Production	Maintenance	Capital expenditure	Marketing
Production wages					
Printing recruitment application forms					
Advertising					
Customer demand survey					
Raw material usage					
Spare parts for production machines					
Warehouse extension					
Commission paid to sales staff					

(d)

Select an appropriate accounting treatment for each of the following costs.

(a)	Holiday pay for production workers	
(b)	Material wastage in the production process	
(c)	Cost of the purchasing department	
(d)	Administrative wages	
(e)	Computing services	
(f)	Production equipment maintenance	
(g)	Depreciation of production equipment	
(h)	Redecoration of the sales showroom	

Options available are:

1   Allocate to marketing overheads

2   Allocate to administrative overheads

3   Direct cost

4   Charge to production in a machine hour overhead rate

5   Charge to production in a labour hour overhead rate

6   Activity based charge to production cost centres

(e)

Calculate the appropriate budgeted overhead recovery rate for the following production department. The department's annual budget for indirect costs is:

	£
Indirect labour	17,000
Supervisor wages	19,000
Depreciation of equipment	4,000
Machine maintenance	3,500
Canteen subsidy	6,500
Total	**50,000**

Notes: The budget production of 2,500 units will require 5,000 machine hours and 25,000 direct labour hours.

Complete the following:

Overhead recovery should be based on **Labour hours / Machine hours / Units produced.**

The recovery rate will be £ [   ] per [   ]

Task 1.2

(a)

Complete the following table to show the forecast inventories and production units for a particular product for weeks 1 to 4.

Units of product P

	Week 1	Week 2	Week 3	Week 4	Week 5
Opening stock	1,200				
Production					
Sub-total					
Sales	6,000	5,000	4,500	5,500	7,000
Closing stock					

Closing stock should be 30% of the following week's forecast sales.

(b)

The quarterly production requirements for product L are shown below.

10% of production fails the quality checks and must be scrapped.

How many items of product L must be manufactured to allow for waste?

	Month 1	Month 2	Month 3
Required units	72,000	90,000	81,000
Manufactured units			

(c)

Raw Material purchases

- 15,000 items of product M are to be manufactured in April.
- Each requires 1.5 metres of raw material.
- 10% of raw material is wasted during manufacture.
- The opening stock will be 12,000 metres.
- The closing stock will be 10,000 metres.

How much material must be purchased?

Select from:

	✓
9,111m	
13,111m	
22,750m	
23,000m	
27,000m	

(d)

Labour hours

- 36,000 units of product L are to be manufactured in May.
- Each one takes 5 minutes to produce.
- 15 staff will each work 180 hours basic time.

How many overtime hours must be worked to complete the production?

Select from:

	✓
180	
300	
360	
3,000	
7,200	

(e)

Department X manufactures three products, A, B and C.

Calculate the machine hours required to manufacture these in November.

Product	Units	Hours per unit	Hours required
A	140	1.5	
B	210	2.0	
C	170	3.0	
Total hours for department X			

There are three machines in the department.

Each machine can be used for 250 hours in November. Additional machines can be hired if required.

How many additional machines should be hired?

Task 1.3

The following production budget for a month has been prepared.

Production Budget	Units
Opening inventory of finished goods	4,000
Production	30,000
Sub total	34,000
Sales	29,000
Closing inventory of finished goods	5,000

(a) Complete the following working schedule for raw materials. Each unit produced requires 0.55 kg of material. Closing inventory is valued at budgeted purchase price.

Raw Materials	kg	£
Opening inventory of raw materials	2,100	2,000
Purchases of raw materials	15,500	27,125
Sub-total	17,600	29,125
Used in production		
Closing inventory of raw materials		

(b) Complete the following working schedule for direct labour. Each unit takes 4 minutes to make. There are 8 direct labour employees, each working 200 basic hours in the month. Additional hours are paid at an overtime rate of time and a half. The overtime premium is included in the direct labour cost.

Direct Labour	Hours	Cost £
Basic time at £12 per hour		
Overtime		
Total		

(c) Complete the following working schedule for overheads. Variable overheads are recovered based on total labour hours worked.

Overheads	Hours	Cost £
Variable overheads at £1.50 per hour		
Fixed overheads		3,400
Total overheads		

(d) Complete the following operating budget, using information from the earlier tasks. Closing inventory of finished goods is to be valued at budgeted production cost per unit.

Operating Budget	Units	£ per unit	£
Sales		2.60	
Cost of Goods Sold:			
Opening inventory of finished goods			7,000
Cost of production:		£	
Raw Materials			
Direct Labour			
Production overheads			
Total cost of production			
Closing inventory of finished goods			
Cost of goods sold			
Gross profit			
Non-production overheads		£	
Administration		3,000	
Marketing		4,000	
Total non-production overheads			
Net profit			

Task 1.4

(a)

This year sales are £1,000,000.

Analysis of recent years shows a growth trend of 5% per annum.

The seasonal variation has been:

Quarter 1	+£25,000
Quarter 2	+£10,000
Quarter 3	−£15,000
Quarter 4	−£20,000

Forecast the sales for each quarter of **next year**.

	£
Quarter 1	
Quarter 2	
Quarter 3	
Quarter 4	
Year	

(b)

Calculate these sales and cost budgets for April.

	Budget for the year	Budget for April
Units sold	24,000	2,000
Units produced	25,000	2,500
	£	£
Sales	480,000	
Materials used	80,000	
Labour	64,800	
Variable production overhead	30,000	
Fixed overhead	1,800	

- Each unit is made from 2 kg of material costing £1.60 per kg.

- It takes 12 minutes to make each item.

- 350 hours of basic time is available in the month. Any extra hours must be worked in overtime.

- The basic rate is £12 per hour. Overtime is paid at time and a half (50% more than basic rate).

- Variable overhead relates to labour hours, including overtime.

- Fixed overhead costs are incurred evenly through the year.

(c)

The following budget data is available:

Budget Data	March £	April £	May £	June £
Invoiced sales	3,000	3,500	3,300	3,800
Purchases	1,000	1,100	1,200	1,100
Wages	500	510	520	480
Other overheads	600	660	620	630
Capital expenditure	0	1,200	0	0

Average terms:

Half of customers take 1 month to pay. Half take 2 months.

Purchases paid for after two months.

Wages paid in the current month.

Other overheads paid after one month.

Capital expenditure paid in the current month.

Complete a cash forecast for May, using the following table.

Cash Forecast - May	£
Opening cash balance	(480)
Customer receipts	
Payments:	
For purchases	
For wages	
For overheads	
For capital expenditure	
Total	
Closing cash balance	

Show payments and receipts as plus figures. Negative balance = overdrawn

Task 1.5

You have prepared a draft budget for direct labour costs.

■ It is based on this year's costs plus an expected pay rise and increased staffing.

■ The manager of human resources has forecast the pay rise.

■ You have calculated the required staffing from the agreed production budget.

■ You have been asked to suggest appropriate performance measures that would assist managers to monitor direct labour performance against budget.

Direct labour budget

	This year	**Next year budget**
Production units	780,000	800,000
Minutes per unit	3.00	3.00
Labour hours	39,000	40,000
Annual hours per staff member	1,800	1,800
Number of staff	22	23
Average salary p.a.	£25,000	£26,500
Direct labour cost	£550,000	£609,500

Write an email (on the following page) to the Production Director:

(a) Explaining the calculations and assumptions and requesting his approval.

(b) Suggesting appropriate direct labour performance indicators for this department.

email

to: Production Director

from: Budget Accountant

date: Today

subject: Review of Operation Statement

Budget submission

Performance indicators

Section 2

Task 2.1

(a)

The company has budgeted to make and sell 100,000 units in the coming year.

Each unit takes 0.5 labour hours to make and requires 2kg of raw material. The quality control department can test 8,000 units each month. A contract has been placed to purchase 150,000kg of raw material at an agreed price. Further supplies can be obtained on the open market but the price is likely to be much higher. The company employs 25 production workers. Each worker works 1,750 hours a year in normal time.

Complete the following analysis.

There is labour available to make _____ units in normal time. Therefore, _____ hours of overtime

will be needed.

The raw material contract will provide enough material to make _____ units.

Therefore, _____ kg will have to be purchased on the open market.

Quality control can test _____ units in the year. It will be necessary to make alternative

arrangements for _____ units.

(b)

From the following data, revise the income forecast.

Next year income is forecast at £7,350,000. This assumes a 5% increase in selling price.

In the light of increasing competition the marketing manager has decided not to make the increase.

The forecast should be revised to....

		✓
(a)	£6,982,500	
(b)	£7,000,000	
(c)	£7,350,000	
(d)	£7,717,500	

(c)

From the following data, revise the forecast for energy costs.

Next year, energy costs are forecast at £228,800. This assumes a 4% increase in energy consumption and a 5% increase in gas and electricity tariffs.

However, energy saving measures are being proposed. Instead of increasing, consumption should be reduced by 10%.

The energy budget should be £…

		✓
(a)	£178,200	
(b)	£198,000	
(c)	£217,800	
(d)	£220,000	

Task 2.2

A monthly operating statement is shown below with some explanatory notes. You are required to flex the budget, calculate variances and show whether each variance is favourable or adverse.

Monthly Operating Statement   Volume 68,000

	Original Budget	Actual	Flexed Budget	Variances Fav / (Adv)
Volume	63,000	68,000		
	£	£	£	£
Turnover	2,520,000	2,856,000		
Costs				
Material	441,000	510,000		
Labour	567,000	616,250		
Distribution	6,300	7,000		
Energy	151,000	164,000		
Equipment hire	32,000	35,000		
Depreciation	182,000	180,000		
Marketing	231,000	235,000		
Administration	186,000	189,000		
Total	1,796,300	1,936,250		
Operating Profit	723,700	919,750		

Notes on budget

■ Material, labour and distribution costs are variable.

■ The budget for energy is semi-variable. The variable element is £2.00 per unit.

■ The budget for equipment hire is stepped, increasing at every 8,000 units of monthly production.

■ Depreciation, marketing and administration costs are fixed.

Task 2.3

You are asked to review the Operating Statement shown below, and the background information provided, and to make recommendations.

	Turnover (units)		1,360,000
Operating Statement for May 2009	**Budget £**	**Actual £**	**Variance £ Fav / (Adv)**
Turnover	2,720,000	2,992,000	272,000
Variable Costs			
Material	816,000	884,000	(68,000)
Labour	612,000	571,200	40,800
Distribution	108,800	111,100	(2,300)
Power	136,000	138,000	(2,000)
Equipment hire	68,000	67,500	500
	1,740,800	1,771,800	(31,000)
Contribution	979,200	1,220,200	241,000
Fixed costs			
Power	14,000	15,000	(1,000)
Equipment hire	10,000	9,000	1,000
Depreciation	108,000	110,000	(2,000)
Marketing	121,000	128,000	(7,000)
Administration	147,000	151,000	(4,000)
	400,000	413,000	(13,000)
Operating Profit	**579,200**	**807,200**	**228,000**

The budget has been flexed to the actual number of units produced and sold. The original budget had been drawn up by the Chief Executive and communicated to senior managers by email.

Despite an unbudgeted price increase, the volume of units sold was higher than expected in the original budget. This seems to have been due to a very successful advertising campaign. Temporary staff had been recruited to avoid overtime costs.

One of the component parts of the product is made from brass which increased in price by 6% for part of the month.

Although pleased with the overall results, the Chief Executive is concerned that costs were above budget and has asked you to advise how control can be improved.

Write an email to the Chief Executive in which you:

(a) Suggest possible reasons for the variances on materials, labour, marketing and administration

(b) Make recommendations on how cost accountability could be improved when setting budgets

email

to: Chief Executive

from: Budget Accountant

date: Today

subject: Review of Operation Statement

Reasons for Variances

Recommendations

Budgeting

Practice assessment 3

Section 1

Task 1.1

(a)

Match the data in the first column with the appropriate source selected from the second column.

Data
Customers who pay promptly
Current raw materials costs
Employers' National Insurance rates

Source
Product life cycle report
Office for National Statistics
HMRC website
Sales ledger
Supplier price lists
Trade association

(b)

Who would you contact in each of the following situations?

(a)	You want to know details of expected future material costs	
(b)	You want to know when the factory extension will be operational	
(c)	You want to know the cost of next year's advertising campaign	

Select from:

1	Factory capital project manager
2	HR Manager
3	Transport Manager
4	Purchasing manager
5	Finance Director
6	Marketing manager

(c)

Complete the following table by using ticks to show into which budget(s) each item of cost would occur. ✓

	Capital Expenditure	Cost of Production	Sales and Marketing	Distribution	Finance
Loan set up fees					
Celebrity product endorsement fees					
Product design royalties					
Purchase of new distribution vehicle					
Agency fees for temporary production labour					
Distribution vehicle fuel					

(d)

Select an appropriate accounting treatment for each of the following costs from the options available.

(a)	Employers' pension contributions for sales staff	
(b)	Product design royalties	
(c)	Repairs to factory roof	
(d)	Cost of maintaining production equipment	
(e)	Cost of sick pay for production operatives	
(f)	Cost of advertising campaign	

Options available are:

1   Allocate to production overheads

2   Allocate to selling and distribution overheads

3   Direct cost

4   Allocate to finance overheads

5   Allocate to marketing overheads

6   Capital expenditure

Task 1.2

(a)

Complete the following table to show the forecast inventories and production units for a particular product.

Closing inventory should be 40% of the following week's forecast sales volume.

Number of Units	Week 1	Week 2	Week 3	Week 4	Week 5
Opening inventory	16,000				
Production					
Sub total					
Forecast sales	40,000	38,500	42,000	39,500	40,000
Closing inventory					

(b)

The production requirements of a product are shown below. 12% of the units produced fail a quality control test and are scrapped. Complete the table to show the number of units that must be manufactured to allow for this rejection rate.

	Month 1	Month 2	Month 3
Required units	93,720	96,272	96,800
Manufactured units			

(c)

The following information is available about the plans for next month.

- 211,500 units of finished product are to be manufactured
- Each unit of finished product contains 2.3 kg of raw material
- 6% of raw material is wasted during manufacture
- The opening inventory of raw material is 48,000 kg
- The closing inventory of raw material is to be 46,500 kg

The purchases of raw material must be

		✓
(a)	96,326 kg	
(b)	484,950 kg	
(c)	514,137 kg	
(d)	516,000 kg	
(e)	519,000 kg	

(d)

90,000 units of finished product are to be manufactured during October. Each unit takes 2.5 minutes to produce. 19 staff each work 190 basic hours in October.

Complete the following sentences:

The number of units that can be made in basic time during October is [   ]

The number of overtime hours required to be worked in October is [   ] hours.

(e)

Department W manufactures three products, Exe, Wye and Zed.

Calculate the machine hours required to manufacture these in November, using the following table.

Product	Units	Hours per unit	Hours required
Exe	450	2.0	
Wye	570	1.2	
Zed	400	1.0	
Total machine hours for department W			

There are seven machines in the department.

Each machine can be used for 290 hours in November. Additional machines can be hired if required.

How many additional machines should be hired?

Task 1.3

The following production budget for a month has been prepared.

Production Budget	Units
Opening inventory of finished goods	5,000
Production	54,000
Sub total	59,000
Sales	50,000
Closing inventory of finished goods	9,000

(a) Complete these three working schedules.

Materials

Each unit produced requires 0.75 kg of material. Closing inventory is valued at budgeted purchase price.

Raw Materials	kg	£
Opening inventory of raw materials	2,300	15,450
Purchases of raw materials	40,000	210,000
Sub total	42,300	225,450
Used in production		
Closing inventory of raw materials		

Direct Labour

Each unit takes 12 minutes to make. There are 55 direct labour employees, each working 170 basic hours in the month. Additional hours are paid at an overtime rate of time and a half. The overtime premium is included in the direct labour cost.

Direct Labour	Hours	Cost £
Basic time at £18 per hour		
Overtime		
Total		

Overheads

Variable overheads are recovered based on total labour hours worked.

Overheads	Hours	Cost £
Variable overheads at £7.00 per hour		
Fixed overheads		40,950
Total overheads		

(b)   Now complete the following operating budget, using information from the earlier tasks. Closing inventory of finished goods is to be valued at budgeted production cost per unit.

Operating Budget	Units	£ per unit	£
Sales		13.00	
Cost of Goods Sold:			
Opening inventory of finished goods			47,500
Cost of production:		£	
Raw Materials			
Direct Labour			
Production Overheads			
Total cost of production			
Closing inventory of finished goods			
Cost of goods sold			
Gross profit			
Non-production overheads		£	
Administration		93,500	
Marketing		48,900	
Total non-production overheads			
Operating profit/(loss)			

Task 1.4

(a)

This year's sales are £3,800,000. Analysis of recent years shows:

■   a negative growth trend of −1.0% per annum

■   seasonal variations from the trend of

   quarter 1   -£4,000

   quarter 2   +£2,000

   quarter 3   +£5,000

   quarter 4   -£3,000

Forecast the sales for each quarter of next year, using the following table.

	£
Quarter 1	
Quarter 2	
Quarter 3	
Quarter 4	
Total Sales	

(b)

Calculate the sales revenue and cost budgets for June from the following data.

- Each unit is made from 1.5 kg of material costing £1.80 per kg.

- It takes 6 minutes to make each item.

- 1,200 hours of basic labour time is available in the month of June. Any extra hours must be worked in overtime.

- The basic labour rate is £14 per hour. Overtime is paid at time and a half (50% more than basic rate).

- Variable overhead relates to labour hours worked, including overtime.

- Fixed overhead costs are incurred evenly through the year.

Complete the following table with the June budget figures.

	Budget for the year	Budget for June
Units sold	144,000	12,500
Units produced	150,000	13,000
	£	£
Sales	792,000	68,750
Cost of production:		
Materials used	405,000	35,100
Labour	220,000	18,900
Variable production overhead	15,000	1,300
Fixed production overhead	24,000	2,000

(c)

The following budget data has been prepared.

Budget Data	June £	July £	August £	Sept £
Invoiced sales revenue	7,300	8,100	7,800	8,200
Purchases	3,450	3,180	3,800	3,900
Wages	1,950	2,000	1,910	2,200
Overheads	1,190	1,200	1,380	1,230
Capital expenditure		4,500	1,900	

Timings:

60% of credit sales are received in the month after sale, the remainder 1 month later

Purchases are paid in the month after purchase

Wages are paid in the month incurred

Overheads are paid in the month after they are incurred. Overheads include £480 per month depreciation

Capital expenditure is paid immediately it is incurred

Complete a cash forecast for August, using the following table.

Cash Forecast - August	£
Opening cash balance	−6,030
Receipts from sales	
Payments for:	
Purchases	
Wages	
Overheads	
Capital expenditure	
Total payments	
Closing cash balance	

Task 1.5

You have prepared a draft budget for direct labour costs.

■ The budget is based on the expected rise in the relevant regional labour cost index of 2.2%, although the company wage negotiations for next year have not yet concluded. This information has been provided by the HR manager.

■ The production manager has confirmed that an efficiency saving of 1% of the labour time required to make each unit is expected due to replacement of some production machinery that is scheduled for the end of the current year.

■ In the current year the direct labour hours have been fulfilled by full time employees, who did not work any overtime.

■ You have calculated the total labour hours required from the agreed production budget.

■ You have been asked to suggest possible inherent risks in the draft budget and its assumptions.

Direct labour budget

	This year	Next year budget
Production units	450,000	440,000
Labour time required to produce 1,000 units	50	49.5
Total labour hours required	22,500	21,780
Hourly rate	£12.50	£12.775
Total labour cost	£281,250	£278,240

Write an email to the Production Director:

(a) Explaining the calculations and assumptions and requesting her approval.

(b) Suggesting possible inherent risks in the draft budget and its assumptions.

email

to:

from:

date:

subject:

Section 2

Task 2.1

A company makes and sells a single product. A first draft operating budget has been prepared for next year. The Marketing Director has suggested that profit might be improved by reducing the selling price, since this could lead to an increased sales volume.

(a)   You are asked to prepare a revised operating budget in the Revision column below, and calculate the increase or decrease in profit that would result.

You should assume that the selling price will be reduced by 10% and the sales volume will increase by 20%.

Draft Operating Budget	First Draft	Revision
Sales units	120,000	
	£	£
Sales price	15.00	
Sales revenue	1,800,000	
Variable production costs	1,320,000	
Fixed production costs	130,000	
Gross profit	350,000	
Increase / (Decrease) in gross profit		

The draft administration salary budget is £187,200. This assumes a 4% pay rise from the beginning of the year. The HR manager has now informed you that the pay rise for administration salaries will be 2.5%.

(b)   Calculate the revised salary budget   £ ⬚

This year's budget for raw materials was set at £319,770. This assumed a 2% price increase from the previous year together with a reduction in production volume of 5%.

However production volume remains static and the price increase is 3%.

(c)   Calculate the raw material cost forecast   £ ⬚

Task 2.2

Reporting results

You are required to complete a monthly operating report for June. The original budget for the month is shown below, followed by relevant notes.

Operating budget for June	£
Sales revenue (50,000 units)	1,450,000
Costs:	
Material	550,000
Labour	325,000
Distribution	190,000
Energy	90,000
Equipment hire	40,000
Depreciation	25,000
Marketing	70,000
Administration	45,000
Total costs	1,335,000
Operating profit	115,000

Notes on budget

■   Material, labour and distribution costs are variable

■   The budget for energy is semi-variable. The fixed element is £30,000

■   Equipment hire budget is based on a cost of £5,000 for each 7,000 units or fewer

■   Depreciation, marketing and administration costs are fixed

Complete the operating report for June shown on the next page with actual figures already inserted. Flex the budget to the actual sales volume and calculate the variances. Show adverse variances with minus signs.

	Flexed Budget £	Actual £	Variances £
Sales revenue (60,000 units)		1,710,000	
Costs:			
Materials		650,000	
Labour		404,000	
Distribution		248,000	
Energy		117,000	
Equipment hire		55,000	
Depreciation		26,000	
Marketing		69,000	
Administration		44,000	
Total Costs		1,613,000	
Operating Profit		97,000	

Task 2.3

The following operating statement has been prepared using marginal costing and a flexed budget.

Operating Statement for November	Budget £	Actual £	Variance £ Fav / (Adv)
Turnover	90,000	94,000	4,000
Variable costs:			
Materials	12,000	15,000	-3,000
Labour	18,000	19,000	-1,000
Distribution	20,000	22,500	-2,500
Power	10,000	13,000	-3,000
Contribution	**30,000**	**24,500**	**-5,500**
Fixed costs:			
Power	5,000	0	5,000
Depreciation	5,500	6,100	-600
Marketing	7,000	3,000	4,000
Administration	4,000	4,000	0
Operating Profit	**8,500**	**11,400**	**2,900**

The original budget was based on producing and selling 2,500 units. The company actually produced and sold 2,000 units, and the budget was flexed to this volume.

You have also established the following information about the operations:

■ the volume of material used was in line with the flexed volume

■ there was some idle time by employees due to the reduced output, but the wage rate was in line with the budget

■ there was an unplanned rise in vehicle fuel prices

■ the company changed power supplier

■ the estimated remaining lives of some non-current assets was reassessed and reduced

■ depreciation is calculated on a straight-line basis

■ a budgeted advertising campaign was scaled down

Write an email to the Managing Director that suggests possible reasons for each of the variances.

email

to:

from:

date:

subject:

Practice assessment 1
– answers

Section 1

Task 1.1   **(a)**

Data		Source
Typical performance in the trade	→	Trade association publications
National economic growth	→	Office for National Statistics
Corporation tax rates	→	HMRC publications

(b)

(a)   **5**

(b)   **4**

(c)   **1**

(c)

	Direct Cost of Production	Production Overheads	Capital Expenditure	Marketing	Cash
Extension to offices			✓		✓
Depreciation of production equipment		✓			
Indirect production labour		✓			✓
Advertising campaign costs				✓	✓
Hire of production equipment		✓			✓
Printing customer perceptions questionnaire				✓	✓

(d)   (a)   **2**

(b)   **3**

(c)   **2**

(d)   **1**

(e)   **6**

(f)   **3**

(e)   Overhead recovery should be based on **Machine hours.**

The recovery rate will be **£16 per machine hour.**

Task 1.2

(a)

Number of Units	Week 1	Week 2	Week 3	Week 4	Week 5
Opening inventory	5,000	5,375	5,250	5,125	5,500
Production	20,375	21,375	20,875	20,875	22,750
Sub total	25,375	26,750	26,125	26,000	28,250
Forecast sales	20,000	21,500	21,000	20,500	22,000
Closing inventory	5,375	5,250	5,125	5,500	6,250

(b)

	Month 1	Month 2	Month 3
Required units	75,330	79,980	77,190
Manufactured units	81,000	86,000	83,000

(c)   (e)   102,000 kg

(d)

The number of units that can be made in basic time during October is 43,200

The number of overtime hours required to be worked in October is 340 hours.

(e)

Product	Units	Units per hour	Hours required
Aye	1,920	8	240
Bee	1,200	2.5	480
Cee	1,400	5	280
Total machine hours for department G			1,000

1 additional machine should be hired.

Task 1.3

(a)

Raw Materials	kg	£
Opening inventory of raw materials	1,800	7,200
Purchases of raw materials	34,000	136,000
Sub total	35,800	143,200
Used in production	35,000	140,000
Closing inventory of raw materials	800	3,200

(b)

Direct Labour	Hours	Cost £
Basic time at £14 per hour	3,200	44,800
Overtime	300	6,300
Total	3,500	51,100

(c)

Overheads	Hours	Cost £
Variable overheads at £9.00 per hour	3,500	31,500
Fixed overheads		24,500
Total overheads		56,000

(d)

Operating Budget	Units	£ per unit	£
Sales	30,000	10.50	315,000
Cost of Goods Sold:			
Opening inventory of finished goods			26,475
Cost of production:		£	
Raw Materials		140,000	
Direct Labour		51,100	
Production Overheads		56,000	
Total cost of production			247,100
Closing inventory of finished goods			8,825
Cost of goods sold			264,750
Gross profit			50,250
Non-production overheads		£	
Administration		18,000	
Marketing		13,500	
Total non-production overheads			31,500
Net profit			18,750

Task 1.4

(a)

	£
Quarter 1	600,625
Quarter 2	660,625
Quarter 3	695,625
Quarter 4	605,625
Total Sales	2,562,500

(b)

	Budget for the year	Budget for May
Units sold	105,000	9,000
Units produced	100,000	8,100
	£	£
Sales	1,260,000	108,000
Cost of production:		
Materials used	700,000	56,700
Labour	175,000	14,250
Variable production overhead	20,000	1,620
Fixed production overhead	48,000	4,000

(c)

Cash Forecast - August	£
Opening cash balance	8,650
Receipts from sales	6,200
Payments for:	
Purchases	2,100
Wages	1,630
Expenses	720
Capital expenditure	2,500
Total payments	6,950
Closing cash balance	7,900

Task 1.5 (a) and (b)

email	
To:	Production Director
From:	Accounting Technician
Date:	xx
Subject:	Direct Material Budget

Budget Submission

I enclose the proposed direct material budget for your consideration and approval.

The production budget is based on a decrease from the current output of 250,000 units to 240,000 units next year, and this assumption has been used for the direct material budget.

The budget assumes the current standard usage of raw material per unit produced of 0.75kg will be reduced by 2% to 0.735kg. This change will be incorporated into the revised standards for next year. The chief buyer has confirmed that the cost price of material is not expected to change next year, and therefore the standard cost per kg will remain the same as the current cost of £7.30 per kg.

Since there is no planned change in the raw material inventory levels, the quantity of material to be purchased will be the same as the budgeted usage.

Please let me know if you need any further information.

Performance Indicators

As the company uses standard costing, the material cost variances will be a very useful performance indicator. The variances are:

• direct material price variance

• direct material usage variance

These variances could be prepared weekly or monthly. The direct material price variance will show the difference in the material cost for the period compared to the standard that is due to the price of material. The direct material usage variance will show the difference that is due to the amount of material used. Since there is an expectation that wastage will be reduced in the next year, the usage variance will be particularly helpful in monitoring this aspect.

Section 2

Task 2.1

(a)

There is labour available to make **52,500** units in normal time. Therefore, **2,500** hours of overtime will be needed.

The raw material contract will provide enough material to make **40,000** units. Therefore, **50,000** kg will have to be purchased on the open market.

Quality control can test **50,400** units in the year. It will be necessary to make alternative arrangements for **9,600** units.

(b)   (c)   £5,157,000

(c)

Current year's usage (kWh)	2,800,000
Next year's usage (kWh)	2,688,000
Current year's price per kWh (£)	0.11
Next year's price per kWh (£)	0.121
Budget for electricity next year (£)	325,248

Task 2.2

	Original Budget	Actual	Flexed Budget	Variances Fav / (Adv)
Volume (units)	90,000	80,000	80,000	
	£	£	£	£
Turnover	1,170,000	1,056,000	1,040,000	16,000
Costs:				
Materials	450,000	410,000	400,000	(10,000)
Labour	360,000	340,000	320,000	(20,000)
Distribution	180,000	155,000	160,000	5,000
Energy	55,000	55,000	50,000	(5,000)
Equipment hire	16,000	15,000	14,000	(1,000)
Depreciation	23,000	24,000	23,000	(1,000)
Marketing	21,000	20,000	21,000	1,000
Administration	25,000	24,000	25,000	1,000
Total Costs	1,130,000	1,043,000	1,013,000	(30,000)
Operating Profit	40,000	13,000	27,000	(14,000)

Task 2.3

---

email

To:	Managing Director
From:	Accounting Technician
Subject:	Operating Statement for November
Date:	xx

I attach the operating statement for November. This has been prepared using a budget flexed to the actual production and sales volume of 1,600 units. This is an increase on the original budget which was based on 1,500 units.

As can be seen from the statement, the actual operating profit was considerably lower than that shown on the flexed budget. The following commentary will suggest possible reasons for each of the variances that analyse this difference.

The adverse turnover variance was caused by selling at a lower average price than budgeted (£82.50 instead of £90). This may have helped increase the sales from the original budget.

It has been established that the price paid for materials was in line with the budgeted price. The favourable material variance must therefore be due to using less material than expected for the output achieved. This could be due to less wastage than was allowed for.

A possible cause of the adverse labour cost variance is the need to use overtime hours, which are traditionally paid at a higher hourly rate than basic hours. The additional hours would be required due to the additional production volume that was achieved.

The changes in the power tariff mean that a greater element of the cost is fixed than budgeted, although the variable element has decreased. Overall the total power cost has increased. Although possible changes in power consumption should be investigated, it seems likely that the variances are caused by the alteration to the tariff.

The actual depreciation charge is lower than that budgeted since the expected remaining lives of some non current assets have been reassessed to a longer period, and the depreciation charge using the straight line basis is therefore reduced. This change can be incorporated into future budgets.

In summary, the overall operating profit adverse variance is mainly accounted for by the reduction in average selling price compared to budget.

Practice assessment 2
– answers

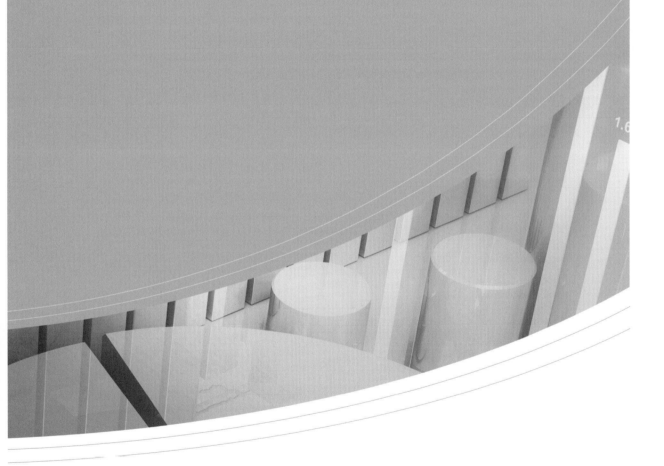

Section 1

Task 1.1

(a)

Data		Source
Inflation trends in UK	➤	Office for National Statistics
Value Added Tax (VAT) rates	➤	HMRC publications (Her Majesty's Revenue & Customs)
Demand for our products	➤	Market Research

(b)

(a)	You want to identify the production capacity of the firm.	5
(b)	You want to forecast the price of raw materials.	3
(c)	The draft budget is ready for review.	4

(c)

	Personnel	Cost of Production	Maintenance	Capital expenditure	Marketing
Production wages		✓			
Printing recruitment application forms	✓				
Advertising					✓
Customer demand survey					✓
Raw material usage		✓			
Spare parts for production machines			✓		
Warehouse extension				✓	
Commission paid to sales staff					✓

(d)

(a)	Holiday pay for production workers	5
(b)	Material wastage in the production process	3
(c)	Cost of the purchasing department	6
(d)	Administrative wages	2
(e)	Computing services	2
(f)	Production equipment maintenance	4
(g)	Depreciation of production equipment	4
(h)	Redecoration of the sales showroom	1

(e)

Overhead recovery should be based on **Labour hours.**

The recovery rate will be **£2 per hour**.

Task 1.2

(a)

Units of product P

	Week 1	Week 2	Week 3	Week 4	Week 5
Opening stock	1,200	1,500	1,350	1,650	
Production	6,300	4,850	4,800	5,950	
Sub-total	7,500	6,350	6,150	7,600	
Sales	6,000	5,000	4,500	5,500	7,000
Closing stock	1,500	1,350	1,650	2,100	

(b)

	Month 1	Month 2	Month 3
Required units	72,000	90,000	81,000
Manufactured units	80,000	100,000	90,000

(c) 23,000m

Working

15,000 items @ 1,5 metres = 22,500m

22,500m x 100 / 90 (wastage) = 25,000

Less 2,000m stock reduction = 23,000m

(d) 300

Working

36,000 x 5/60 = 3,000 hrs basic time

3,000 – (15 x 180) = 300 hrs overtime

(e)

Product	Units	Hours per unit	Hours required
A	140	1.5	210
B	210	2.0	420
C	170	3.0	510
Total hours for department X			1,140

2 additional machines should be hired.

Task 1.3

(a)

Raw Materials	kg	£
Opening inventory of raw materials	2,100	2,000
Purchases of raw materials	15,500	27,125
Sub-total	17,600	29,125
Used in production	16,500	27,200
Closing inventory of raw materials	1,100	1,925

(b)

Direct Labour	Hours	Cost £
Basic time at £12 per hour	1,600	19,200
Overtime	400	7,200
Total	2,000	26,400

(c)

Overheads	Hours	Cost £
Variable overheads at £1.50 per hour	2,000	3,000
Fixed overheads		3,400
Total overheads		6,400

(d)

Operating Budget	Units	£ per unit	£
Sales	29,000	2.60	75,400
Cost of Goods Sold:			
Opening inventory of finished goods			7,000
Cost of production:		£	
Raw Materials		27,200	
Direct Labour		26,400	
Production overheads		6,400	
Total cost of production			60,000
Closing inventory of finished goods			10,000
Cost of goods sold			57,000
Gross profit			18,400
Non-production overheads		£	
Administration		3,000	
Marketing		4,000	
Total non-production overheads			7,000
Net profit			11,400

Task 1.4

(a)

	£
Quarter 1	287,500
Quarter 2	272,500
Quarter 3	247,500
Quarter 4	242,500
Year	1,050,000

(b)

	Budget for the year	Budget for April
Units sold	24,000	2,000
Units produced	25,000	2,500
	£	£
Sales		40,000
Materials used		8,000
Labour		6,900
Variable production overhead		3,000
Fixed overhead		150

(c)

Cash Forecast - May	£
Opening cash balance	(480)
Customer receipts	3,250
Payments:	
For purchases	1,000
For wages	520
For overheads	660
For capital expenditure	0
Total	2,180
Closing cash balance	590

Task 1.5

email
To: Production Director
From: Budget Accountant
Date: Today
Subject: Review of Operation Statement

Budget submission

I attach the proposed direct labour budget for next year for your consideration and approval.

The agreed production plan indicates an increase in volume to 800,000 units next year. No change in productivity has been assumed. Therefore, the staffing level needs to increase by one to 23.

The manager of human resources estimates that average pay will increase by 6% next year to £26,500.

Please let me know if you need any further information.

Performance indicators

There are a range of useful measures to monitor cost, efficiency, effectiveness, and employee satisfaction. Staff hours and output data should be available on a daily basis. Labour rates are reviewed periodically. However, employee satisfaction is probably best canvassed once or twice a year. I recommend that we conduct a weekly review of performance based on:

·   Minutes per unit

·   Hours of overtime

·   Percentage of good output (or similar quality measure)

·   Average hourly rate

We should also commission a confidential employee satisfaction and involvement questionnaire.

A Technician

Section 2

Task 2.1

(a)

There is labour available to make **87,500** units in normal time. Therefore, **6,250** hours of overtime will be needed.

The raw material contract will provide enough material to make **75,000** units. Therefore, **50,000** kg will have to be purchased on the open market.

Quality control can test **96,000** units in the year. It will be necessary to make alternative arrangements for **4,000** units.

(b)

The forecast should be revised to **(b) £7,000,000**.

(c)

The energy budget should be **(b) £198,000**.

Task 2.2

<table>
<tr><th colspan="2">Monthly Operating Statement</th><th colspan="3">Volume 68,000</th></tr>
</table>

	Original Budget	Actual	Flexed Budget	Variances Fav / (Adv)
Volume	63,000	68,000		
	£	£	£	£
Turnover	2,520,000	2,856,000	2,720,000	136,000
Costs				
Material	441,000	510,000	476,000	(34,000)
Labour	567,000	616,250	612,000	(4,250)
Distribution	6,300	7,000	6,800	(200)
Energy	151,000	164,000	161,000	(3,000)
Equipment hire	32,000	35,000	36,000	1,000
Depreciation	182,000	180,000	182,000	2,000
Marketing	231,000	235,000	231,000	(4,000)
Administration	186,000	189,000	186,000	(3,000)
Total	1,796,300	1,936,250	1,890,800	(45,450)
Operating Profit	723,700	919,750	829,200	90,550

Task 2.3

---

email

To: Chief Executive

From: Budget Accountant

Date: Today

Subject: Review of Operation Statement

Reasons for Variances

I have reviewed the results for May 2009. Profit in the month was £807,200 driven by a 10% price improvement over budget and increased volume. After flexing the original budget to allow for the increased volume, we are reporting adverse expense variances of £44,000.

The only significant favourable expense variance is labour. This is one cost which you might expect to be adverse because increased workloads tend to create high overtime costs. This was avoided by using temporary workers and cost savings were made.

Material costs were 8% over budget. The increase in brass costs does not adequately explain this variance. We need to investigate whether the use of temporary workers, and the demotivating impact of this on the permanent staff, may have led to higher levels of material wastage. It may be preferable to use our own staff at overtime rates.

Marketing costs were £7,000 over budget, no doubt due to the costs of the advertising campaign, and this seems to be money well spent.

The administration overspend is worrying and needs to be investigated. It could have been a one-off. Alternatively, perhaps there are variable costs such as overtime or bonus that should not have been budgeted as fixed costs.

Recommendations

Budgets are useful for planning, coordination, authorisation and control. However, this requires the full and enthusiastic involvement of the management team. I suggest that you need to:

*   Involve the whole team in the planning process.
*   Insist that all known factors and plans (such as the advertising campaign) are built into the budget.
*   Assign responsibilities to individuals for all aspects of the budget.
*   Allow managers freedom to manage their budgets.

Practice assessment 3 answers

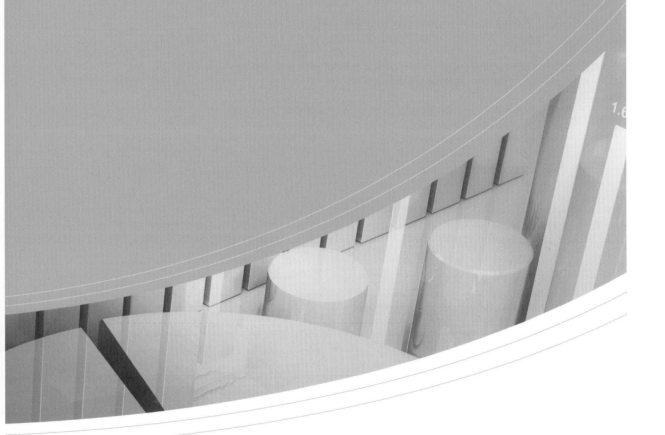

Section 1

Task 1.1

(a)

Data	Source
Customers who pay promptly	Sales ledger
Current raw materials costs	Supplier price lists
Employers' National Insurance rates	HMRC website

(b)

(a) You want to know details of expected future material costs
4 Purchasing manager

(b) You want to know when the factory extension will be operational
1 Factory capital project manager

(c) You want to know the cost of next year's advertising campaign
6 Marketing manager

(c)

	Capital Expenditure	Cost of Production	Sales and Marketing	Distribution	Finance
Loan set up fees					✓
Celebrity product endorsement fees			✓		
Product design royalties		✓			
Purchase of new distribution vehicle	✓				
Agency fees for temporary production labour		✓			
Distribution vehicle fuel				✓	

(d)

(a) Employers' pension contributions for sales staff
  2 Allocate to selling and distribution overheads

(b) Product design royalties
  3 Direct cost

(c) Repairs to factory roof
  1 Allocate to production overheads

(d) Cost of maintaining production equipment
  1 Allocate to production overheads

(e) Cost of sick pay for production operatives
  1 Allocate to production overheads

(f) Cost of advertising campaign
  5 Allocate to marketing overheads

Task 1.2

(a)

Number of Units	Week 1	Week 2	Week 3	Week 4	Week 5
Opening inventory	16,000	15,400	16,800	15,800	
Production	39,400	39,900	41,000	39,700	
Sub total	55,400	55,300	57,800	55,500	
Forecast sales	40,000	38,500	42,000	39,500	40,000
Closing inventory	15,400	16,800	15,800	16,000	

(b)

	Month 1	Month 2	Month 3
Required units	93,720	96,272	96,800
Manufactured units	106,500	109,400	110,000

(c) (d) 516,000 kg

(d)

The number of units that can be made in basic time during October is **86,640**

The number of overtime hours required to be worked in October is **140** hours.

(e)

Product	Units	Hours per unit	Hours required
Exe	450	2.0	900
Wye	570	1.2	684
Zed	400	1.0	400
Total machine hours for department W			1,984

No additional machines should be hired.

Task 1.3

(a) Complete these three working schedules.

Materials

Raw Materials	kg	£
Opening inventory of raw materials	2,300	15,450
Purchases of raw materials	40,000	210,000
Sub total	42,300	225,450
Used in production	40,500	216,000
Closing inventory of raw materials	1,800	9,450

Direct Labour

Direct Labour	Hours	Cost £
Basic time at £18 per hour	9,350	168,300
Overtime	1,450	39,150
Total	10,800	207,450

Overheads

Overheads	Hours	Cost £
Variable overheads at £7.00 per hour	10,800	75,600
Fixed overheads		40,950
Total overheads		116,550

(b)

Operating Budget	Units	£ per unit	£
Sales	50,000	13.00	650,000
Cost of Goods Sold:			
Opening inventory of finished goods			47,500
Cost of production:		£	
Raw Materials		216,000	
Direct Labour		207,450	
Production Overheads		116,550	
Total cost of production			540,000
Closing inventory of finished goods			90,000
Cost of goods sold			497,500
Gross profit			152,500
Non-production overheads		£	
Administration		93,500	
Marketing		48,900	
Total non-production overheads			142,400
Operating profit / (loss)			10,100

Task 1.4

(a)

	£
Quarter 1	936,500
Quarter 2	942,500
Quarter 3	945,500
Quarter 4	937,500
Total Sales	3,762,000

(b)

	Budget for the year	Budget for June
Units sold	144,000	12,500
Units produced	150,000	13,000
£	£	
Sales	792,000	68,750
Cost of production:		
Materials used	405,000	35,100
Labour	220,000	18,900
Variable production overhead	15,000	1,300
Fixed production overhead	24,000	2,000

(c)

Cash Forecast - August	£
Opening cash balance	−6,030
Receipts from sales	7,780
Payments for:	
Purchases	3,180
Wages	1,910
Overheads	720
Capital expenditure	1,900
Total payments	7,710
Closing cash balance	-5,960

Task 1.5

---

email

To   Production Director   From   Budget Accountant

Subject   Direct Labour Budget   Date

(a)   Budget submission

I attach the proposed direct labour budget for next year for your consideration and approval.

The agreed production plan is based on a reduction in output from 450,000 units this year to 440,000 units next year.

A reduction in the time taken to produce each unit of 1% compared to the current year has been allowed for. This is an anticipated efficiency saving due to the use of some new machinery that is shortly to be installed.

An increase in the current labour rate has been incorporated into the budget. This increase of 2.2% is in line with the forecast regional labour cost index.

The total direct labour cost for next year is £278,240 based on these assumptions.

Please let me know if you need any further information.

(b)   Inherent risks

The various assumptions built into the budget could prove to be inaccurate and this would result in risks to the budget. These include:

- The budget is based on 440,000 units being produced. If this forecast is inaccurate then it will impact on the direct labour costs.

- The budget assumes that the direct labour requirement is entirely in proportion to the production level. If there is a part of the labour requirement that does not behave in this way (for example the time taken to set up production runs may form a stepped-fixed cost) then the hours required may differ from the budget.

- Since the total number of direct labour hours required is fewer than this year there could be costs involved in transferring staff to other duties or even redundancy costs.

- Installation of the planned new machinery could be delayed which would reduce or eliminate the expected efficiency saving of 1%. If the machinery is installed on time the efficiency saving may not be as expected.

- The wage rate increase is based on the expected rise in the regional labour cost index. This index may prove an unreliable estimate of the costs that this company incurs, which will depend on the company wage negotiations which have not yet concluded.

Section 2

Task 2.1

(a)

Draft Operating Budget	First Draft	Revision
Sales units	120,000	144,000
	£	£
Sales price	15.00	13.50
Sales revenue	1,800,000	1,944,000
Variable production costs	1,320,000	1,584,000
Fixed production costs	130,000	130,000
Gross profit	350,000	230,000
(Decrease) in gross profit		(120,000)

(b)   The revised salary budget is **£184,500**

(c)   The raw material cost forecast is **£339,900**

Task 2.2

Reporting results

	Flexed Budget £	Actual £	Variances £
Sales revenue (60,000 units)	1,740,000	1,710,000	-30,000
Costs:			
Materials	660,000	650,000	10,000
Labour	390,000	404,000	-14,000
Distribution	228,000	248,000	-20,000
Energy	102,000	117,000	-15,000
Equipment hire	45,000	55,000	-10,000
Depreciation	25,000	26,000	-1,000
Marketing	70,000	69,000	1,000
Administration	45,000	44,000	1,000
Total Costs	1,565,000	1,613,000	-48,000
Operating Profit	175,000	97,000	-78,000

Task 2.3

email			
To	Managing Director	From	Budget Accountant
Subject	Review of Operating Statement	Date	

Reasons for Variances

The sales volume was lower than the original budget planned, with sales at 2,000 units instead of the expected 2,500 units. The budget has been flexed to the actual level of 2,000 units and variances calculated accordingly.

The revenue variance reveals a price increase from the budgeted £45 per unit to an average £47 per unit. This resulted in a favourable variance of £4,000. There may be a link between the increased price and the volume reduction from first budgeted, and there could also be a link with the reduced advertising noted below.

The materials used were in line with expectations for the revised volume, so the adverse variance of £3,000 must be due to an average buying price of £7.50 per unit compared with the budgeted £6 per unit. This needs to be investigated.

The reduced level of output created some idle time amongst the labour force. This increased the labour cost per unit to £9.50 from the budgeted £9.00 despite the wage rate being as planned.

There was a change in power supplier which resulted in reduced power costs overall. Although the variable cost of power increased from £5 to £6 per unit produced, the new supplier does not impose a fixed charge. This resulted in an overall favourable power variance of £2,000.

The depreciation charge for the year was adjusted upwards to account for a review of non-current asset lives in which the estimated remaining useful lives of some assets was reduced. This resulted in an adverse variance of £600.

The planned advertising campaign was scaled back and this saving resulted in a favourable variance of £4,000. However, in combination with the selling price increase, this may have contributed to the reduction in sales volume. An analysis of this area should be undertaken to establish the most profitable policy.

The administration costs were in line with the budget.

Overall the operating profit was £2,900 greater than the flexed budget showed, since the favourable variances related to sales revenue. Power and marketing outweighed the various adverse variances.